Sounds Of The Sixties

A Whiter Shade Of Pale *Procol Harum*
Mr Tambourine Man *Bob Dylan/Byrds*
Lucy In The Sky With Diamonds *The Beatles*
God Only Knows *The Beach Boys*
Waterloo Sunset *The Kinks*
Nights In White Satin *The Moody Blues*
I've Got To Get A Message To You *Bee Gees*
(I Can't Get No) Satisfaction *The Rolling Stones*
All You Need Is Love *The Beatles*
Blowin' In The Wind *Bob Dylan*
Light My Fire *The Doors*
Catch The Wind *Donovan*
My Generation *The Who*
Proud Mary *Creedence Clearwater Revival*

Wise Publications
London/New York/Paris/Sydney/Copenhagen/Madrid

Exclusive Distributors:
Music Sales Limited
8/9 Frith Street,
London W1V 5TZ, England.
Music Sales Pty Limited
120 Rothschild Avenue,
Rosebery, NSW 2018,
Australia.

Order No.AM91293
ISBN 0-7119-3533-5
This book © Copyright 1993 by Wise Publications

Compiled by Peter Evans
Book design by Pearce Marchbank, Studio Twenty
Computer management by Adam Hay Editorial Design

Printed in the United Kingdom by
J.B. Offset Printers (Marks Tey) Limited,
Marks Tey, Essex.

Your Guarantee of Quality
As publishers, we strive to produce every book to the
highest commercial standards.
The book has been carefully designed to minimise
awkward page turns and to make playing from it a real
pleasure. Particular care has been given to specifying
acid-free, neutral-sized paper which has not been
chlorine bleached but produced with special regard for
the environment.
Throughout, the printing and binding have been planned
to ensure a sturdy, attractive publication which should
give years of enjoyment.
If your copy fails to meet our high standards, please
inform us and we will gladly replace it.

Music Sales' complete catalogue lists thousands of titles
and is free from your local music shop, or direct from
Music Sales Limited. Please send a
cheque/postal order for £1.50 for postage to:
Music Sales Limited, Newmarket Road,
Bury St. Edmunds, Suffolk IP33 3YB.

A Whiter Shade Of Pale

Words & Music by Keith Reid & Gary Brooker.

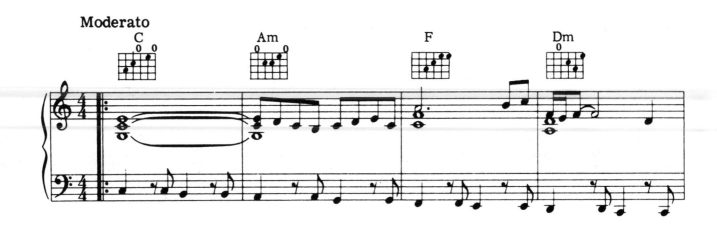

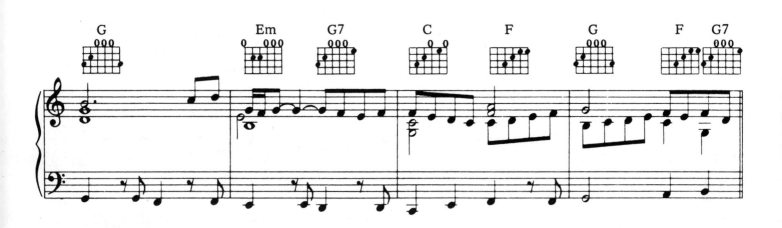

We skipped the light fan - dan-go   And turned cartwheels _'cross the

She said,"There is   no   rea-son,   And the   truth is __ plain to

floor.—
see.",—

I was feel-ing kind of sea-sick,
But I wan-dered through my play-ing cards

But the crowd called out for more,
And would not— let her be.

The room was humming har-der
One of six-teen vest-al vir-gins

As the cei-ling flew a - way.—
Who were lea-ving for the coast,—

When we called out for a - no - ther drink
And al-tho' my eyes were o - pen

5

The wai-ter brought a tray,— And so it was _____ that la-ter

They might just as well been closed,

As the mil-ler told his tale,—

That her face at first just

ghostly, Turned a whi-ter ___ shade of pale.___ pale.___

Mr Tambourine Man

Words & Music by Bob Dylan.

brand - ed on my feet. I have no one to meet And the

an - cient emp - ty street's too dead for dream - in'. _____

Repeat 3 times

Refrain:

Verse 2. Take me on a trip upon your magic swirlin' ship
My senses have been stripped, my hands can't feel to grip
My toes too numb to step, wait only for my boot heels
To be wanderin'
I'm ready to go anywhere, I'm ready for to fade
Into my own parade, cast your dancin' spell my way
I promise to go under it.

Refrain:

Verse 3. Though you might hear laughin' spinnin' swingin' madly across the sun
It's not aimed at anyone, it's just escapin' on the run
And but for the sky there are no fences facin'
And if you hear vague traces of skippin' reels of rhyme
To your tambourine in time, it's just a ragged clown behind
I wouldn't pay it any mind, it's just a shadow you're
Seein' that he's chasin'.

Refrain:

Verse 4. Then take me disappearin' through the smoke rings of my mind
Down the foggy ruins of time, far past the frozen leaves
The haunted, frightened trees out to the windy beach
Far from the twisted reach of crazy sorrow
Yes, to dance beneath the diamond sky with one hand wavin' free
Silhouetted by the sea, circled by the circus sands
With all memory and fate driven deep beneath the waves
Let me forget about today until tomorrow.

Refrain:

Lucy In The Sky With Diamonds

Words & Music by John Lennon & Paul McCartney.

1. Pic - ture your -
2. Fol - low her
3. Pic - ture your -

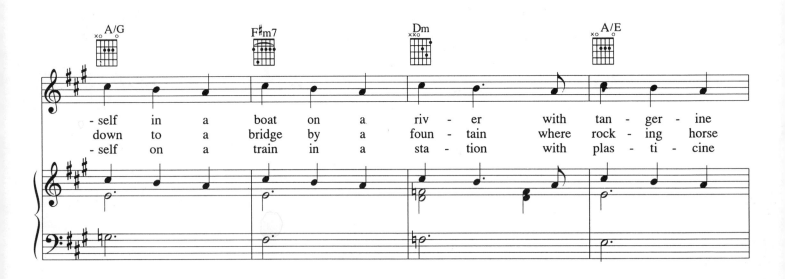

-self in a boat on a riv - er with tan - ger - ine
down to a bridge by a foun - tain where rock - ing horse
-self on a train in a sta - tion with plas - ti - cine

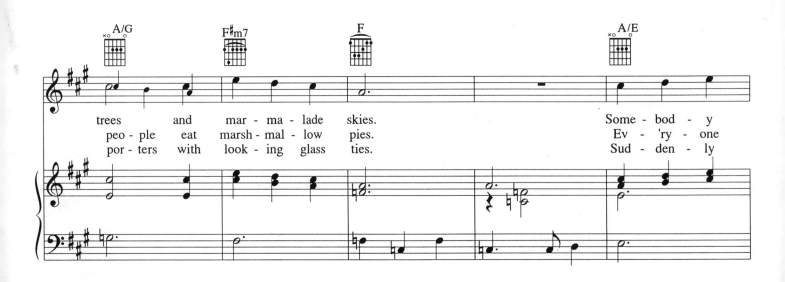

trees and mar - ma - lade skies. Some - bod - y
peo - ple eat marsh - mal - low pies. Ev - 'ry - one
por - ters with look - ing glass ties. Sud - den - ly

calls you, you an- swer quite slow- ly, a girl with ka-
smile as you drift past the flow- ers that grow so in-
some- one is there at the turn- stile, the girl with ka-

To Coda ⊕

-lei- do- scope eyes. _____
-cred- ib- ly high. _____
-lei- do- scope

Cel- o- phane flow- ers of yel- low and green,
News- pa- per tax- is ap- pear on the shore,

tow- er- ing o- ver your head. _____ Look for the
wait- ing to take you a- way. _____ Climb in the

Sun and
G D7 Em

11

girl with the sun in her eyes and she's gone.
back with your head in the clouds and you're gone.

Lu - cy in the sky with dia - monds, Lu - cy in the sky with dia - monds, Lu - cy in the sky with dia - monds,

Ah.

Ah.

D.S. al Coda

Coda

eyes.

12

God Only Knows

Words & Music by Brian Wilson & Tony Asher.

Waterloo Sunset

Words & Music by Raymond Douglas Davies.

Nights In White Satin

Words & Music by Justin Hayward.

I've Got To Get A Message To You

Words & Music by Barry Gibb, Robin Gibb & Maurice Gibb.

(I Can't Get No) Satisfaction

Words & Music by Mick Jagger & Keith Richards.

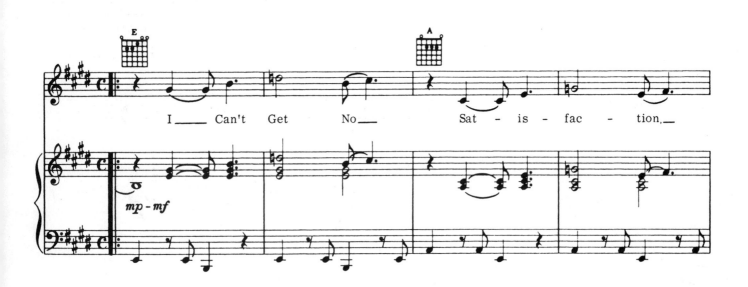

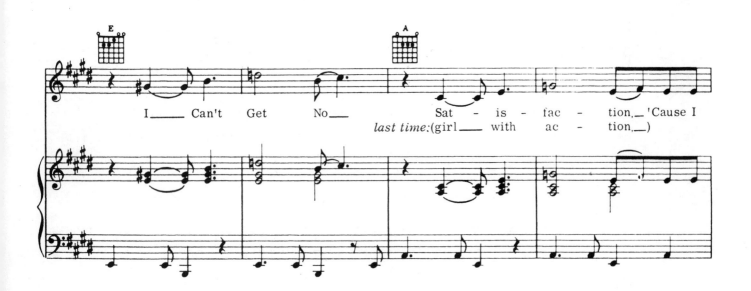

try ____ and I try ____ and I try ____ and I try.___ I can't

get no... I can't get no...

{ 1.When I'm
{ 2.When I'm
{ 3.When I'm

driv-in' in my car,___ And that man comes on the ra - di - o; And he's
watch-in' my T. V.,___ And that man comes on to tell__ me;__ How__
rid - in' 'round the world,_ And I'm do - in' this and I'm sign - in' that; And I'm

tell-in' me more and more_ a-bout some use - less in - for-ma - tion, Sup-posed to____
white_ my shirts can be,_____ Well, he can't be a man, 'cause he_ does-n't smoke the____
try-in' to make some girl._Who tells me, "Ba-by, bet-ter come back lat - er next week, 'cause you

fire_ my im-ag - i - na - tion,
same cig-a- rettes as me._____ }   I can't   get   no,   Oh, no, no,
see I'm on a los - ing streak."_

no,   Hey, hey,   hey_   that's what I   say.___

I can't get no,   I can't

get no,   I Can't Get No   Sat-is -

fac - tion,   No Sat-is - fac - tion,   No Sat-is -

fac - tion,   No Sat-is - fac - tion.

fade out

All You Need Is Love

Words & Music by John Lennon & Paul McCartney.

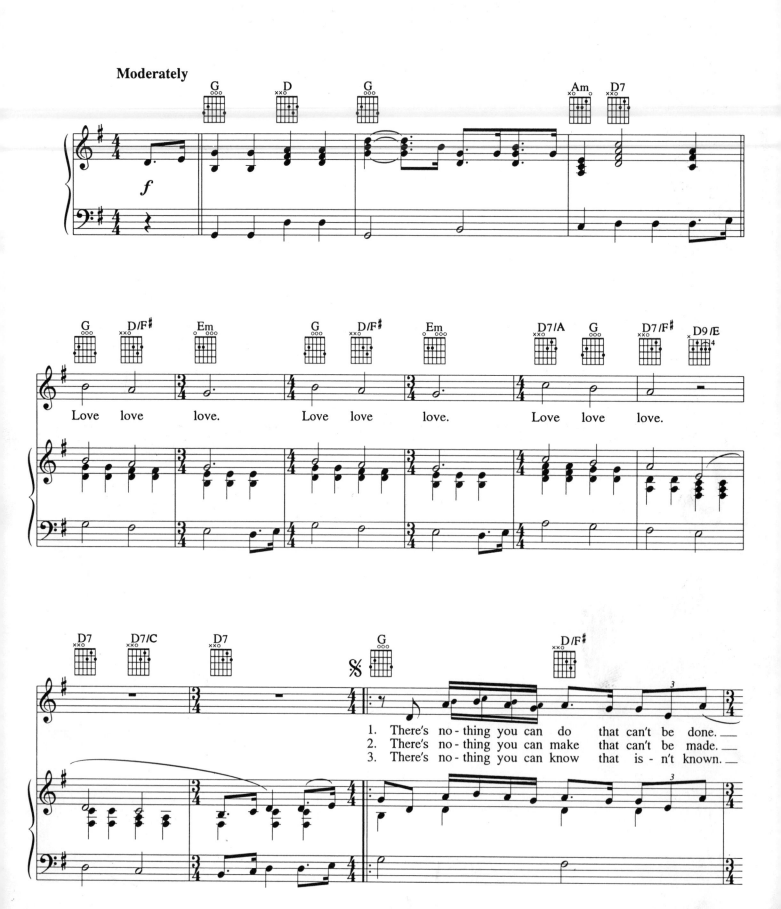

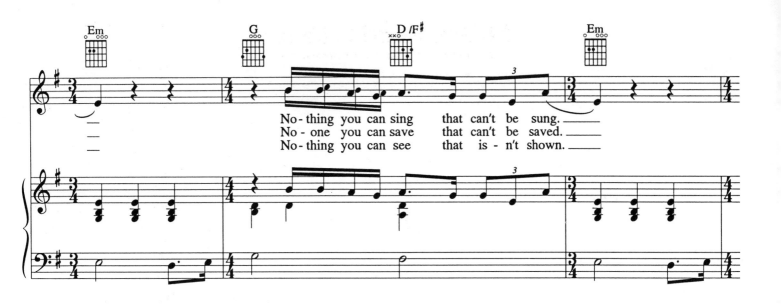

No-thing you can sing that can't be sung. ___
No-one you can save that can't be saved. ___
No-thing you can see that is-n't shown. ___

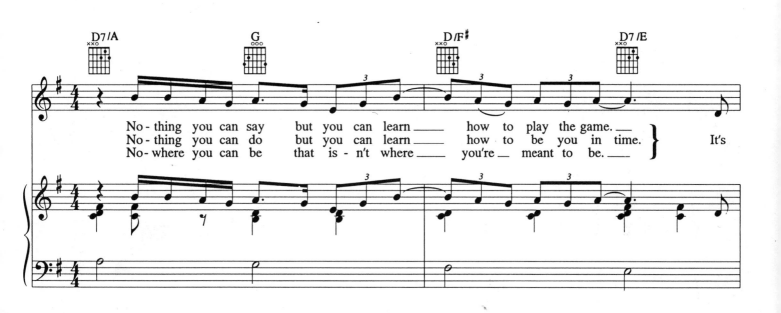

No-thing you can say but you can learn ___ how to play the game. ___
No-thing you can do but you can learn ___ how to be you in time. ___
No-where you can be that is-n't where ___ you're ___ meant to be. ___

It's

ea - sy.

All you need is love, ___

29

Blowin' In The Wind

Words & Music by Bob Dylan.

seas   must   a   white   dove ___ sail   be - fore   she
ears _____ must   one - man ___ have   be - fore   he can

sleeps   in   the   sand?   Yes, 'n' how   man - y
hear   peo - ple   cry?   Yes, 'n' how   man - y

times   must   the   can-non - balls   fly   be - fore   they're
deaths   will   it   take   'til   he   knows d   and   that too   man - y

for - ev - er   banned?   The   an - swer, my
peo - ple   have   died?

Additional Lyrics

3. How many years can a mountain exist
before it is washed to the sea?
Yes 'n' how many years can some people exist
before they're allowed to be free?
Yes 'n' how many times can a man turn his head
pretending that he just doesn't see?

The answer, my friend, is blowin' in the wind,
The answer is blowin' in the wind.

Light My Fire

Words & Music by The Doors.

1. You know that it would be un - true;
2. (The) time to hes - i - tate is through,

You know that I would be a liar;
No time to wal - low in the mire,

If I was to say to you;
Try now we can on - ly lose, And our

love be-come a fune-ral pyre.___ Come on, ba - by, light my fire,_

Come on, ba - by, light my fire,_____

Try to set the night on fire,_____ Try to set the night on

fire.___

Catch The Wind

Words & Music by Donovan.

In the warm ___ hold of your lov - in' mind, ___
Ah, but I may as well try and

To catch the wind.

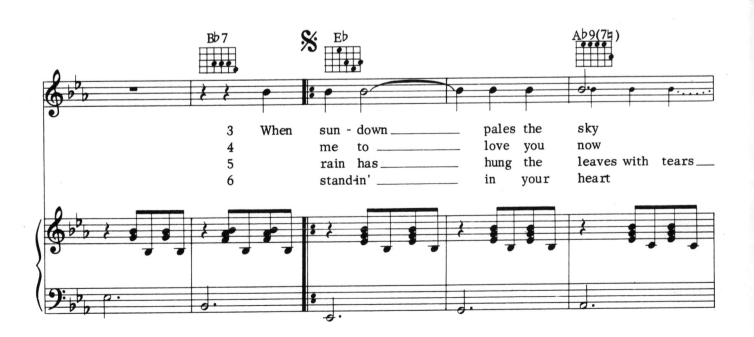

3 When sun - down ___ pales the sky
4 me to ___ love you now
5 rain has ___ hung the leaves with tears ___
6 standin' ___ in your heart

I   want   to   'bide   a - while ___   be - hind   your smile; __
would   be   the   sweet - est thing, ___   t'would   make   me   sing; __
___   I   want   you near ___   to   kill   my   fears, __
is   where I   want   to   be, ___   and   long   to   be;

And   ev - 'ry - where   I'd   look,   your   eyes   I'd   find. _____
Ah,   but   I   may   as   well   try   and
To   help   me   to   leave   all   my   blues   be - hind. _____
Ah,   but   I   may   as   well   try   and

For   catch   the   wind.

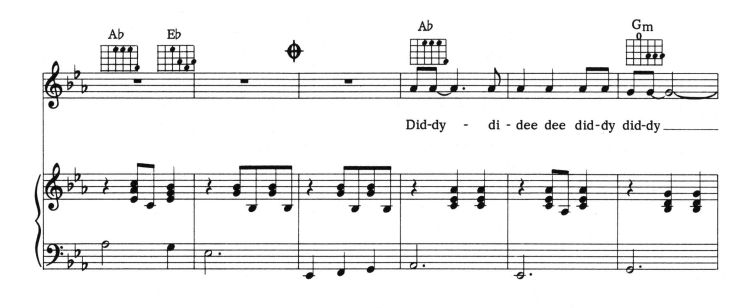

Did-dy - di - dee dee did-dy did-dy____

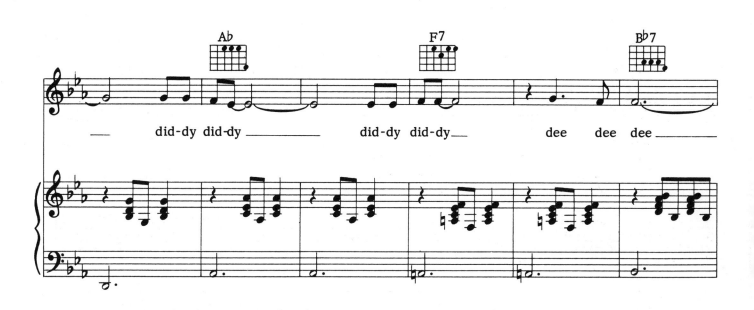

____ did-dy did-dy _____ did-dy did-dy___ dee dee dee _____

D.S. al ⊕ 𝄋

Coda

When

My Generation

Words & Music by Pete Townshend.

not tryin' to cause a big sen - sa - tion. I'm just
[Talk - in' 'bout my gen - er - a - tion]

talk - in' 'bout my gen - er - a - tion._____ This is my gen-er-
[Talk - in' 'bout my gen - er - a - tion]

a - tion,_____ This is my gen-er-a - tion, ba - by._____

Proud Mary

Words & Music by John C. Fogerty.

Moderately, with a heavy beat

Verse
G

Left a good job — in the ci - ty, —
Cleaned a lot of plates in Mem-phis,

Work-in' for The Man ev-'ry night and day, — And I ne-ver lost one min -
Pumped a lot of pain in New Or - leans, — But I ne-ver saw the good-

-ute of sleep-in', Wor-ry-in' 'bout the way things might have been._
___ side of the ci-ty Un - til I hitched a ride on a riv - er boat queen._

Chorus

Big wheel_ keep on _ turn-in', _ Proud Ma-ry keep on burn - in', _ Roll-

-in', _ roll - in', _ roll - in' on the riv - er. ___

If you come down to the riv-er, Bet you gon-na find some peo - ple who live.

D.S. al ⊕ 𝄋

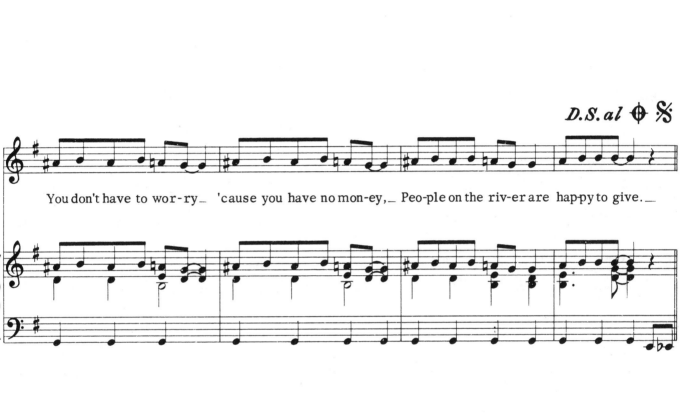

You don't have to wor-ry 'cause you have no mon-ey, Peo-ple on the riv-er are hap-py to give.

⊕ *Coda*

repeat and fade

Roll-in', roll - in', roll-in' on the riv - er.